STAR WARS™
Stories of the
Jedi and Sith

LONDON, NEW YORK, MUNICH,
MELBOURNE, AND DELHI

Senior Editor Catherine Saunders
Brand Manager Lisa Lanzarini
Publishing Manager Simon Beecroft
Category Publisher Siobhan Williamson
DTP Designer Santosh Kumar Ganapathula
Production Nick Seston
Reading Consultant
Linda Gambrell

Lucasfilm Ltd.
Executive Editor Jonathan Rinzler
Art Director Troy Alders
Continuity Editor Leland Chee
Director of Publishing Carol Roeder

This edition published in the United States in 2010

First published in the United States in 2007 and 2008 as four separate titles: *Star Wars: I Want To Be a Jedi 2007, Star Wars: The Story of Darth Vader 2008, Star Wars: Epic Battles 2008 and Star Wars: Beware the Darkside 2007*

Published in the United States by
DK Publishing, Inc., 375 Hudson Street,
New York, New York 10014

10 11 10 9 8 7 6 5 4 3 2 1

Page design copyright © 2007, 2008 Dorling Kindersley Limited.
Copyright © 2007, 2008, 2010 Lucasfilm Ltd and ™.
All rights reserved. Used under authorization.

Published in Great Britain by Dorling Kindersley Limited.

A catalog record for this book is available
from the Library of Congress.

ISBN: 978-0-7566-7067-2

Color reproduction by GRB Editrice S.r.l., London
Printed and bound by L-Rex, China.

Discover more at
www.dk.com

www.starwars.com

STAR WARS™
Stories of the
Jedi and Sith

Contents

★STAR WARS★ ™
I WANT TO BE A
JEDI

Written by Simon Beecroft

Mace Windu

Obi-Wan Kenobi

The Jedi

If you want to be a Jedi, you must learn all about Jedi ways. You must train hard. The Jedi are the best fighters in the galaxy, but their job is to keep the peace. A Jedi trains hard for many years. Then he or she travels around the galaxy to wherever there is trouble. The Jedi do all they can to bring peace without using violence.

A Jedi learns about a powerful energy field called the Force. The Force is everywhere. A Jedi must be able to understand and use the Force.

Yoda

Great Power
The Force is a special energy. You cannot see it, but you can learn to feel it. Yoda, a Jedi, uses the Force to help others in the galaxy.

Jedi usually go on missions in pairs.

Long Training

To be a Jedi, you must start your training when you are very young. First you will be a Youngling. If you pass the tests, you become a Padawan Learner. This means you are training to be a Jedi, but you are not a Jedi yet. If you train hard for several years and pass more tests, you will become a Jedi Knight.

When you are a Padawan you will go on missions, but never alone. A more experienced Jedi will always go with you. A Jedi Master is the most experienced Jedi of all. One day, if you continue to learn and train, you too could become a Jedi Master. Then you will train other, younger Jedi apprentices. This is how the Jedi Order works.

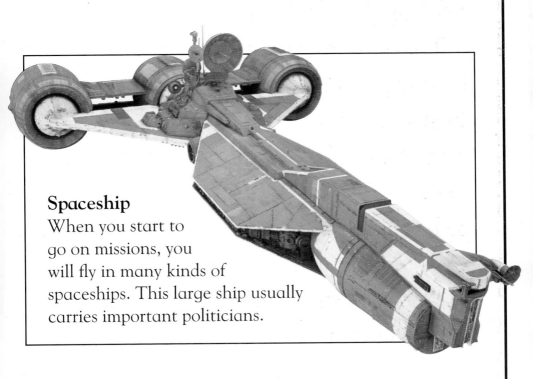

Spaceship
When you start to go on missions, you will fly in many kinds of spaceships. This large ship usually carries important politicians.

Special Powers

Jedi can come from anywhere in the galaxy. When they are very young, a boy or girl discovers that they have a special power. Perhaps they can move objects with their mind or they can do something really fast. They are using the Force without realizing it. This means that they could be a good Jedi.

One such person was Anakin Skywalker. Although he was very young, he was a great pilot. He flew a very fast machine called a Podracer and won a very dangerous race. A Jedi Master called Qui-Gon Jinn (pronounced KWY-GONN-JIN) met Anakin and decided to train him to be a Jedi. Qui-Gon Jinn thought that Anakin could become a great Jedi.

Anakin Skywalker is determined to win the Podrace.

Jedi in Training

When you begin training to be a Jedi you must leave your home and your parents. It's hard to leave behind everyone you love, so you must really want to be a Jedi. You travel from your home to a big planet at the center of the galaxy. A building called the Jedi Temple will be your home for the rest of your life. Here is where your Jedi training begins.

A New Home
The Jedi Temple is a gigantic building where all Jedi live, train, and work. It contains training halls, meeting rooms, libraries, and huge hangars for spaceships.

Using a training device, Jedi Master Yoda teaches the Younglings how to "see" without using their eyes.

At the Jedi Temple, you have many classes to learn all the Jedi skills. You learn to control your emotions so that you do not feel fear, anger, or hatred. You learn to use the Force. Sometimes, you will wear a special training helmet that covers your eyes. You will to learn to "see" only by using the Force.

Master and Learner

When you are training to be a Jedi, you spend a lot of time with your teacher. Your teacher will be a Jedi Master. You will travel everywhere together. You must always be prepared to learn from your teacher.

Anakin Skywalker's teacher was called Obi-Wan Kenobi (pronounced OH-BEE-ONE KEN-OH-BEE). Anakin felt that Obi-Wan was holding him back.

Anakin does not always listen to what Obi-Wan Kenobi tells him.

Anakin believes that Chancellor Palpatine is a good man and listens to his advice.

Anakin was impatient to become a Jedi Knight. He was more powerful than most Jedi, but he did not always obey the rules of the Jedi Order. Anakin shared his feelings of frustration with Chancellor Palpatine (pronounced PAL-PA-TEEN). Anakin thought that Palpatine was a good friend to him.

Forbidden Marriage

Like everyone, the Jedi can fall in love, but they must not allow any strong emotions to get in the way of defending the galaxy. The Jedi are forbidden to marry because strong emotional attachments can cloud their judgment and stop them from doing their jobs well.

Anakin Skywalker knew that he was not allowed to get married, but he fell in love with a beautiful woman called Padmé Amidala (pronounced PAD-MAY AM-EE-DAL-AH). Anakin and Padmé secretly got married. If anyone found out that Anakin was married, he would have to stop being a Jedi.

The Jedi Council

The most powerful and wise Jedi sit
on the Jedi High Council. Their job is to
make all the most important decisions.
Twelve Jedi sit on the Council at any one
time. The Jedi Council meets in one of
the tall towers of the Jedi Temple. Two of
the most important members of the Jedi
Council are Yoda and Mace Windu.

Yoda is a very wise, green-skinned alien who is many hundreds of years old. Mace Windu is a human Jedi with great powers of thought. Yoda and Mace are both highly skilled with the Jedi's only weapon, which is called a lightsaber.

Mace Windu

Lightsabers

Lightsabers work like swords, but the blade is not made of metal. A lightsaber blade is made of glowing energy that can be many different colors. It is much more powerful than a metal blade, so a Jedi must learn how to use it safely and carefully. This is an important part of a Jedi's training.

Qui-Gon protects Queen Amidala from a battle droid.

Jedi must never use their lightsabers to attack others. They must use them only to defend and protect. Jedi are taught to respect life in any form.

Jedi build their own lightsabers, so every lightsaber is different. If you lose your lightsaber you must build another one yourself.

Lightsaber handle
You hold your lightsaber by the handle. When you activate it, the blade comes out of the end. The blade can slice through almost anything.

Lightsaber Combat

The Jedi use their lightsabers to defend themselves and others. Lightsabers can stop objects or deflect blaster fire. They can slice open sealed doors. Sometimes a Jedi has to fight someone else with a lightsaber. The Jedi use many fast moves to block their opponent. They use the Force to make their movements faster.

They also use the Force to guess what moves their opponent will make, even before they have made them.

Jedi Master Qui-Gon fights a deadly enemy named Darth Maul.

Mind Tricks

The Jedi can use the Force to influence the actions of other people. With a special wave of the hand, a Jedi can tell a person what he or she wants them to think or do. The person repeats back what the Jedi has just said, unaware that the Jedi has put the thought in their mind. This is called a Jedi mind trick.

Jedi mind tricks only work on certain people. They do not work on everyone. Certain strong-willed people can resist the Jedi mind trick.

All in the Mind
Once Obi-Wan used a Jedi mind trick on a small-time criminal. He convinced the crook to start living an honest life.

Anakin Skywalker used to be a slave
owned by a flying alien called Watto.
Qui-Gon tried to free Anakin by using
a mind trick on Watto, but Watto could
not be influenced.

Mind Powers

Jedi can also use the Force to move objects without touching them. For a Jedi, there is no difference between a large object and a small object. A skilled Jedi can move objects of any size—large or small.

Great Teacher
Yoda taught a young Jedi called Luke Skywalker how to lift heavy objects using the Force. At first Luke found it hard to believe it was possible.

Wise Jedi like Yoda can lift very heavy objects using their mind alone. Yoda can lift heavy rocks and even raise a spaceship out of a swamp!

Jedi mind powers are also useful if a Jedi drops his lightsaber in a battle. He can quickly make it jump back into his hand using the Force.

Jedi Equipment

The Jedi carry certain special tools when they go on a mission. They never know what they might need! They carry their tools on a special belt called a utility belt. They can hang their lightsaber on their utility belt. The belt also holds a medical kit, tools, food capsules, and a special communication device called a comlink. The Jedi use comlinks to send and receive messages.

Qui-Gon uses his comlink to speak with Obi-Wan Kenobi.

Comlink

Qui-Gon uses his holoprojector to show realistic pictures of a spaceship.

Another useful Jedi device is called a holoprojector, which enables a Jedi to record an image and then play it back later. A holoprojector can also transmit a moving image of yourself to someone else, like a video link.

Holoprojector

Special Missions

Special missions require special equipment. If you are going to swim underwater for long periods of time, you will need a Jedi breather. It fits into your mouth so you can breathe air through it. It holds enough air to last for two hours. Qui-Gon Jinn and Obi-Wan Kenobi once used breathers to reach an underwater city on the planet of Naboo.

Another useful device is a pair of macrobinoculars. They electronically zoom in on objects that are very far away. They even work in the dark!

Tracer Beacon

If you want to keep track of a suspect, you could stick a tracer beacon to their spaceship. It sends signals that enable you to follow the spaceship.

Darth Sidious

Deadly Enemies

The Jedi's deadly enemies are called the Sith. The first Sith were once Jedi, but they turned bad. Most Jedi use the Force for good but the Sith use the dark side of the Force to gain greater powers. The Sith want to destroy the Jedi.

A long time ago, the Sith and the Jedi fought a war. The Jedi defeated the Sith—or so they thought. Unknown to the Jedi, one Sith Master survived. The Sith Master secretly trained one other person so his skills would be passed on when he died. For a thousand years, each Sith Master trained one other person to keep the Sith skills alive. The final Sith Master was called Darth Sidious (pronounced SID-EE-US). He planned to destroy the Jedi once and for all.

Sith Battles

Sidious trained a ferocious alien called Maul. Maul had tattoos all over his head and horns on his skull. His teeth were razor sharp and his eyes were yellow. Maul fought with a deadly lightsaber with two blades, one at each end. He was a very fast fighter and the dark side of the Force gave him terrifying strength.

The Sith use lightsabers with red blades.

Sidious sent Maul to kill Qui-Gon and Obi-Wan. Maul killed Qui-Gon, but he was eventually defeated by Obi-Wan.

Dooku

When Maul was killed, Sidious had to find someone else to train. He found a Jedi Master called Dooku. Dooku had left the Jedi order and could not resist the chance to become a Sith.

Unusual Enemy

The Jedi and the Sith are usually
the only people who uses lightsabers.
However, the Sith Count Dooku trained
a man-droid to use a lightsaber.
His name was General Grievous
(pronounced GREE-VUS). General
Grievous fought with stolen lightsabers.
Each time he killed a Jedi in battle,
he took the Jedi's lightsaber.

Grievous was a deadly foe because his two mechanical arms could split into four. This meant he could fight with four lightsabers at the same time. During a war in the galaxy, Grievous fought Obi-Wan Kenobi. Grievous wanted to kill Obi-Wan and steal his lightsaber. The battle was ferocious, but in the end Obi-Wan managed to defeat Grievous.

War!

For thousands of years the Jedi were peacekeepers in the galaxy. The Jedi had no idea that the Sith were planning to destroy them. Anakin's friend Chancellor Palpatine was actually the Sith Lord Sidious. Sidious created huge armies of droids and started a war in the galaxy.

The first battle was on a dusty red planet called Geonosis (pronounced GEE-O-NO-SIS). The droid armies attacked the Jedi. Massive tanks on giant legs walked across the battlefield, firing all the time. Many Jedi were killed. Next, the droid armies began to attack planets, one after another.

Jedi Knight, Aayla Secura, goes into battle on a boggy world covered in giant fungus plants.

Brave Generals

When war began, the Jedi had to stop the droid armies from attacking every planet in the galaxy. There were far fewer Jedi in the galaxy than droid armies. Many Jedi became great generals. Yoda was commander of all the armies, with Mace alongside him.

The Jedi fought battles on many strange planets. Aayla Secura (pronounced AY-LA SEK-URE-RAH) went to a planet covered in dense jungles to stop an enemy attack. Ki-Adi-Mundi (pronounced KEE-ADDY-MUNDY) led an army to a dangerous enemy planet covered with crystals.

Ki-Adi-Mundi is a Jedi Master of great power and skill.

Jedi Pilots

The Jedi are some of the best pilots in the galaxy. Often they use their Force powers when they are flying spaceships.

Anakin Skywalker is one of the best pilots in the galaxy. He can fly at top speed using his Force powers. The Jedi can fly many kinds of vehicles, including flying cars called airspeeders. Once, Obi-Wan piloted an underwater ship called a bongo!

Anakin uses all his Jedi skills to fly an airspeeder through a busy city.

*Obi-Wan pilots his Jedi starfighter away
from danger.*

When the Jedi go on missions, they often
fly small ships called starfighters. There is
just enough space for the Jedi
pilot and a small droid.

Pilot Droids
Pilot droids sit in
spaceships with Jedi and
help them to reach their
destination. This droid is
called R2-D2.

Space Battle

During the war in the galaxy, Jedi flew small attack ships called Interceptors. They are faster than ordinary starfighters. During a crucial space battle of the war, hundreds of spaceships fought each other. Anakin made many brave attacks in his Interceptor.

Obi-Wan flew close by Anakin in his own ship. Obi-Wan's ship was hit by enemy fire. Although he was in great danger, he managed to land his ship and get out just in time!

Anakin and Obi-Wan fly into the heart of the space battle.

Dark Side

The worst thing a Jedi can do is to turn away from the good side of the Force and begin using the dark side. One of the most powerful Jedi of all, Anakin Skywalker, turned to the dark side during the war. The evil Sith Lord Sidious persuaded Anakin to join him and become a Sith.

Anakin turned away from his loving wife, Padmé, and attacked the Jedi Temple. He killed many Jedi. Anakin even tried to kill his oldest friend and teacher, Obi-Wan. Obi-Wan did not want to fight his old friend, but he had no choice. It took all his strength and powers, but in end he thought he had killed Anakin. He was wrong.

A New Era

The war was the most dangerous time the galaxy had ever seen. Millions of people died, including nearly all of the Jedi. The evil Sith Lords won the war and ruled the galaxy. Anakin also survived and ruled alongside Emperor Palpatine. Now he was called Darth Vader and he wore a black helmet.

Darth Vader has the body of Anakin Skywalker, but he has turned to the dark side of the Force.

Luke Skywalker never thought he
would become a Jedi, but he did.

A few Jedi survived. They hid until
the time was right to destroy the Sith.
They were led by Anakin's
children, Luke and Leia. After
many long battles, the Sith
were destroyed.

As long as there are
Jedi, there is hope for the
galaxy. May the Force be
with you!

Luke Skywalker is the son
of Anakin and Padmé.

Glossary

Airspeeder
A type of flying car.

Apprentice
A person who is learning a skill.

Blaster
A gun that fires a deadly beam of light.

Comlink
A communication device that sends and receives messages.

Dark side
The part of the Force associated with fear and hatred.

Droid
A kind of robot. R2-D2 is a droid.

Empire
A group of nations ruled over by one leader, who is called an Emperor. Palpatine is the Emperor who rules the Galactic Empire.

The Force
An energy field created by all living things.

Galactic
Something from or to do with a galaxy.

Galaxy
A group of millions of stars and planets.

Holoprojector
A device that records still or moving images.

Interceptors
A type of Jedi attack ship that is faster than a starfighter.

Jedi Knight
A *Star Wars* warrior with special powers who defends the good of the galaxy. Anakin Skywalker, Luke Skywalker, and Ob-Wan Kenobi are all Jedi Knights.

Jedi Master
The most experienced Jedi of all.

Jedi Order
The name of a group that defends peace and justice in the galaxy.

Jedi Temple
The Jedi headquarters where the Jedi Council meets and Jedi live, train, and work.

Lightsaber
A Jedi's and Sith's weapon, made of

glowing energy.

Light side
The part of the Force associated with goodness, compassion and healing

Macrobinoculars
Binoculars that electronically zoom in on objects far away, even in the dark.

Missions
Special tasks or duties.

Padawan Learner
A Jedi who is learning the ways of the Force.

Republic
A nation or group of nations in which the people vote for their leaders.

Sith
Enemies of the Jedi who use the dark side of the Force.

Starfighter
A small, fast spaceship used by Jedi and others.

Youngling
The first stage of Jedi training, before you become a Padawan Learner.

STAR WARS™
THE STORY OF
DARTH VADER

Written by Catherine Saunders

The Story of Darth Vader

Take a look at Darth Vader—if you dare! He is a very dangerous man with many terrifying powers. Darth Vader is a ruthless Sith Lord who helps rule the galaxy for the evil Emperor Palpatine.

But Darth Vader was not always the masked Sith you see now. Once he was a talented Jedi Knight named Anakin Skywalker. Read on and uncover the story of how a promising young Jedi turned to the dark side of the Force.

Emperor Palpatine
From the first moment he met Anakin Skywalker, Palpatine knew that he could be the perfect apprentice.

Young Anakin Skywalker

Anakin Skywalker grew up a slave on the desert planet Tatooine. His mother Shmi could not explain how Anakin came to be born—he had no father.

Anakin was a gentle child and he loved his mother very much. From a young age he was skilled at making and fixing mechanical things. When he was nine years old he built a droid named C-3PO to help his mother. However, Anakin was impulsive and liked to take risks.

Slave owner
Anakin and Shmi were owned by a junk dealer named Watto and had to do whatever he told them. Watto made them work very hard.

A Special Calling

When Jedi Qui-Gon Jinn and Obi-Wan Kenobi landed on Tatooine to repair their damaged ship, they met Anakin Skywalker. Qui-Gon realized the young slave had the potential to be a great Jedi.

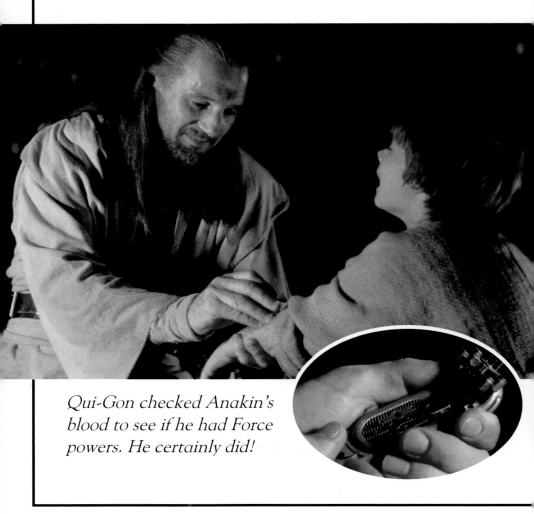

Qui-Gon checked Anakin's blood to see if he had Force powers. He certainly did!

When Anakin offered to enter a
dangerous Podrace, Qui-Gon seized the
opportunity to win the parts he needed
for his ship and Anakin's freedom. The
Jedi was sure that Anakin's Force powers
would help him to win the race. He was
right. Freed from slavery, Anakin was
able to leave Tatooine with the Jedi, but
first he had to say goodbye to his mother.

Anakin was happy to be embarking on a new adventure, but he missed his mother very much.

A New Life Begins

After leaving Tatooine, Qui-Gon asked the Jedi Council to let Anakin become his apprentice, but it refused. The Council thought that Anakin was already too old, and some wise members also sensed danger in Anakin's future.

So, when Qui-Gon and Obi-Wan went on a special mission, Anakin went too.

Padmé Amidala
Queen Padmé Amidala of
Naboo was only a few years
older than Anakin and the
young boy developed strong
feelings for her.

Anakin and the Jedi liberated the
planet Naboo from the Trade Federation
invasion. When Anakin piloted a
starfighter and destroyed the Trade
Federation's Droid Control Ship, the Jedi
Council changed its mind. Although Qui-
Gon had been killed by a Sith, Obi-Wan
promised to train Anakin instead.

Jedi Training

Anakin Skywalker returned to the Jedi Temple on the capital planet Coruscant to begin his training. He was taught how to use and control his incredible Force powers. Anakin was also instructed in the ways of the Jedi Knights. Jedi must be calm and not governed by emotions. They are peace-loving and use their skills only to defend, never to attack.

As Jedi Master Obi-Wan Kenobi's Padawan learner or apprentice, Anakin came to view Obi-Wan as the closest thing he had to a father figure.

The Force
The energy known as the Force is everywhere. Jedi learn to use the light side of the Force for good, while their enemies, the Sith, use the dark side for greed and power.

Increasing Frustration

Anakin loved and respected Obi-Wan, but often felt frustrated by him. Anakin was confident in his Jedi abilities, and felt that Obi-Wan was holding him back. He was tired of being just a Padawan.

Obi-Wan knew that Anakin had the potential to be a powerful Jedi Knight.

But he also believed that Anakin had not yet mastered his emotions, as a Jedi should. Obi-Wan was proved right when Anakin was reunited with Padmé Amidala after ten years. The feelings that Anakin had felt for her as a boy had not gone away. Soon he would no longer be able to control them.

Powerful Friend

The galaxy was formed as a Republic, which meant that it was ruled by a Senate in which all the planets had representatives. As his frustration grew, Anakin found himself turning to Chancellor Palpatine, leader of the Republic. Palpatine seemed to understand exactly how Anakin felt. He was a good listener. Anakin believed that Palpatine was on his side, unlike Obi-Wan.

Sith Lord
Palpatine was secretly a Sith Lord, Darth Sidious. He served as Supreme Chancellor of the Republic—but he had plans to destroy it.

Anakin did not realize that Palpatine was secretly trying to destroy the Republic and seize power for himself.

Unstoppable Feelings

Palpatine's sinister influence increased Anakin's frustration with Obi-Wan and the Jedi Order and left him feeling very confused. When he was chosen to escort Padmé back to Naboo, he finally lost the battle to control his feelings for her.

Padmé was now a Senator and had a
duty to the Republic, but she too could
not prevent herself from falling in love
with Anakin. They were secretly married
on Naboo. Jedi were not supposed to get
emotionally attached to others. Anakin
had broken the rules, but he didn't care.

Turning to the Dark Side

Anakin had not forgotten his mother Shmi, whom he had left on Tatooine. He began to have terrible nightmares about her, so he went to find her.

Out of Control
As he knelt by Shmi's grave, Anakin was angry that he could not save her. He had ignored the Jedi teachings and given into his anger.

Anakin went back to Tatooine. There he discovered that Shmi had married a farmer named Cliegg Lars, who had freed her from slavery. Anakin also learned that his mother had been kidnapped by Sand People. He went in search of her but he was too late and she died in his arms. Overcome with grief and anger, Anakin took revenge on the Sand People.

Jedi Hero

Although he was increasingly ruled by his emotions, Anakin had not yet fully turned to the dark side. When the Republic was forced into the Clone Wars, Anakin fought bravely with the Jedi.

The Clone Wars lasted for many years and Anakin and Obi-Wan became famous heroes. Anakin felt truly alive in the heat of the battle and his powers became even stronger.

However, Anakin still felt that he was being held back by the Jedi and that only Palpatine was encouraging his talents. Anakin felt that maybe the Jedi teachings were not right and that greater power lay elsewhere.

The Shadow of Death
Padmé became pregnant and Anakin began to have nightmares about her death. He had been unable to save his mother, so he was determined to save Padmé.

The Dark Side Wins

Towards the end of the Clone Wars,
Palpatine was kidnapped. Anakin and
Obi-Wan went to his aid, but it was
a trap. Sith Lord Count Dooku was
waiting for them. He knocked out
Obi-Wan and began to fight Anakin.
Palpatine urged Anakin to kill Dooku
and Anakin gave in.

A short time later Anakin chose Palpatine over the Jedi and his transition to the dark side was complete. He knelt before Palpatine—his new Sith Master.

On Palpatine's orders, Anakin led an attack on the Jedi Temple.

The End of Anakin

Anakin turned his back on the Jedi and adopted the Sith name Darth Vader. On Palpatine's orders he set out to destroy his former friends and comrades. Darth Vader also became convinced that Padmé and Obi-Wan were plotting against him. He nearly killed his wife and then faced Obi-Wan in an intense lightsaber battle.

Although Darth Vader was driven by anger and the power of the dark side, Obi-Wan won the terrible fight. Vader suffered horrific injuries and burns.

Anakin the Sith
When he turned to the dark side, Anakin's eyes turned yellow like all the Sith. He could no longer hide his alliance with evil.

Rebuilding Darth Vader

Although Darth Vader's body seemed beyond repair, Palpatine refused to give up on his evil apprentice. He took Vader's body to a secret medical facility where it was rebuilt using cyber-technology. Vader needed special breathing equipment and life support systems just to stay alive.

Behind the black armor and a black helmet, it seemed that no part of the human Anakin Skywalker was left. Darth Vader had given himself completely to the ways of the dark side.

Palpatine and his clone troopers recovered Darth Vader's broken body from the volcano planet Mustafar.

Padmé's Secret

With her husband lost to the dark side, a heartbroken Padmé gave birth to twins, whom she named Luke and Leia. Loyal Jedi Master Obi-Wan Kenobi was by her side, but Padmé had no will to live without Anakin.

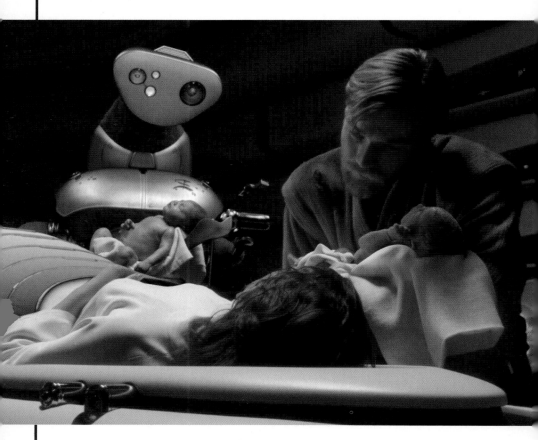

Reunited
At first Luke and Leia had no idea that they were twins, but they felt a special connection. When they discovered the truth, they were happy and not completely surprised.

Jedi Master Yoda decided to keep the children a secret from their father. Obi-Wan took Luke to Tatooine to live with Shmi Skywalker's stepson Owen Lars and his wife Beru. Luke's life on the desert planet was hard and lonely. Leia, was taken to the planet Alderaan. She was adopted by Obi-Wan's friend Bail Organa and brought up a princess. Neither twin knew that the other existed. They did not suspect that their father was the feared Sith Lord Vader.

The Rise of Darth Vader

The Republic had been destroyed and the evil Palpatine ruled the galaxy as Emperor, with Vader by his side. The Sith Lords would let nothing and no one stand in their way. Darth Vader's terrifying appearance, deep voice, and loud artificial breathing struck fear into the hearts of his enemies and allies alike. Even his own generals could not escape Vader's wrath and, as time went by, the Sith's powers grew even stronger.

Anakin Skywalker had been a brave pilot and highly skilled with a lightsaber, but the dark side of the Force continued to corrupt the mind of Darth Vader. He would strangle people without even touching them and he could read the thoughts and feelings of others.

Civil War

Although the Sith had destroyed the Republic and most of the Jedi, a small group of Rebels bravely opposed the Empire. Known as the Rebel Alliance, they were based on the planet Yavin 4. Little did Darth Vader know that two of the Rebels were his children, Luke and Leia.

The famous Jedi Master Obi-Wan Kenobi faced his former apprentice once again. This time Obi-Wan let Darth Vader win in order to show Luke that, thanks to the Force, a person's spirit continues after death.

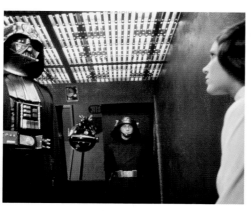

Torture
When Darth Vader captured the Rebel Princess Leia, he tortured her to learn the Rebels' secrets. He had no idea that she was his own daughter.

Rebel Victory

The Emperor decided to build a superweapon known as a Death Star. It was the size of a small moon and had the power to blow up entire planets. However, the Rebels managed to obtain the plans for the weapon and learned that it had a fatal flaw.

One exhaust port was
unprotected and if a pilot
fired torpedoes into its shaft, a
chain reaction of explosions would destroy
the whole Death Star. The Rebels sent a
squadron of star fighters and their best
pilot, Luke Skywalker, had one chance to
destroy the Death Star. He did not miss.

Imperial Fleet

The Rebel Alliance had only a small
number of ships which already bore
the scars of previous battles, but the
Empire had a massive fleet of starships.
The largest and most powerful Imperial
vessels were known as Super Star
Destroyers. Powered by thirteen engines,
the Super Star Destroyers were arrow
shaped and loaded with deadly weapons.

Darth Vader's ship *Executor* was the most powerful Super Star Destroyer. Vader commanded the fleet, but the Emperor gave his orders via hologram.

Executor
Vader's magnificent ship led the Imperial fleet into many great battles. It was eventually destroyed by the Rebels.

Vader's Revenge

When the Rebels blew up the first Death Star, it made Darth Vader and the Emperor extremely angry. They began building a new Death Star and Darth Vader set out to find and destroy the Rebels responsible. Vader sent probe droids to every corner of the galaxy to find the Rebels' new base. He finally located them on the ice planet Hoth.

Although Darth Vader won the Battle of Hoth, he was not able to destroy the Rebels' best ship, the Millenium Falcon.

The Sith Lord traveled to Hoth with the Imperial fleet and launched a deadly attack. The Rebels had to evacuate very quickly and their forces were scattered far and wide across the galaxy.

Luke Skywalker

After having a vision in which his friends were in danger, Luke Skywalker flew to Cloud City, near the gas planet Bespin. He was now more powerful thanks to the teachings of Jedi Master Yoda.

Cloud City

Emperor Palpatine had finally told Darth Vader the truth about Luke Skywalker. As Darth Vader laid a trap for Luke on Cloud City, he was looking for more than just a troublesome Rebel— he was searching for his son.

As Luke and Vader fought with lightsabers, Luke still had no idea who lay behind Darth Vader's mask. The fight ended when Vader chopped off Luke's hand. He revealed that he was Luke's father and asked his son to join him and rule the galaxy. Despite his painful wound, Luke was strong with the Force. He refused to turn to the dark side.

Vader's Choice

For many years, Darth Vader had been loyal to Emperor Palpatine. However, meeting his son Luke—a good and true person—seemed to change him. Could it be that some part of Anakin Skywalker remained behind Vader's mask?

Palpatine had predicted that Luke would come to them and he would be turned to the dark side. When Luke surrendered, it seemed that Palpatine would be proved right. As father and son fought once more, Luke felt anger and hatred and drew close to the dark side. At the last moment Luke was able to control his feelings and refused to join the dark side. As an enraged Palpatine attacked Luke, Anakin Skywalker finally returned from the dark side to save his son.

Death of an Emperor
As Palpatine tortured Luke with deadly Force lightning, Darth Vader could not bear to watch. He picked up his Master and threw him down a bottomless reactor shaft. The Emperor was dead!

The Death of Darth Vader

At the vital moment, Darth Vader returned from his nightmare. Luke had reminded him that he was once a great Jedi named Anakin Skywalker. However, as Vader saved his son, he was fatally wounded by the Emperor.

As Anakin lay dying, he asked Luke to remove his helmet so that he could look at his son's face with his own eyes. When Anakin died, his body disappeared into the light side of the Force. Luke was sad that his father was dead but proud of him too. The light side of the Force had overcome the dark side and Anakin Skywalker had returned.

On the forest moon of Endor, Luke burned Vader's armor. All around the galaxy, everyone celebrated the end of Palpatine and his evil Empire.

Jedi Restored
After his death, Anakin took his place with the other great Jedi heroes Yoda and Obi-Wan Kenobi.

Glossary

Apprentice
A person who is learning a skill.

Dark side
The part of the Force associated with fear and hatred.

Droid
A kind of robot.

Emperor
The leader of an Empire is called an Emperor. Palpatine is the Emperor who rules the Galactic Empire.

Empire
A group of nations ruled over by one leader, who is called an Emperor.

The Force
An energy field created by all living things.

Force lightning
One of the Sith's powers which involves firing deadly electricity from their fingers.

Galaxy
A group of millions of stars and planets.

Jedi Council
The governing body

of the Jedi order. The wisest Jedi, such as Yoda, sit on the Council.

Jedi Knight
A *Star Wars* warrior with special powers who defends the good of the galaxy. Anakin Skywalker, Luke Skywalker, and Ob-Wan Kenobi are all Jedi Knights.

Jedi Master
The most experienced Jedi of all.

Jedi Order
The name of a group that defends peace and justice in the galaxy.

Jedi Temple
The Jedi headquarters where the Jedi Council meets and Jedi live, train, and work.

Lightsaber
A Jedi's and Sith's weapon, made of glowing energy.

Light side
The part of the Force associated with goodness, compassion, and healing.

Missions
Special tasks or duties.

Padawan Learner
A Jedi who is learning the ways of the Force.

Rebel
Someone who opposes whoever is in power.

Republic
A nation or group of nations in which the people vote for their leaders.

Senate
The governing body of the Republic.

Senator
A member of the Senate. He or she will have been chosen (elected) by the people of his or her country.

Sith
Enemies of the Jedi who use the dark side of the Force.

Slave
A person who is owned by another person.

Starfighter
A small, fast spaceship used by Jedi and others.

STAR WARS™
EPIC BATTLES

Written by Simon Beecroft

What side are you on?

A long time ago, in a galaxy far, far away, a great and peaceful Republic existed. Each planet, large or small, made its voice heard in a huge Senate building on the capital planet, Coruscant. The Jedi Knights defended peace and justice everywhere. They ensured that arguments between planets were sorted out without violence or war.

Jedi Knights
The Jedi use a mysterious energy called the Force. Jedi Knights carry glowing lightsabers to defend themselves.

Battle droids
The Trade Federation built many millions of machine-soldiers called battle droids. Each battle droid carries a deadly blaster weapon.

Sadly, this peace was about to be smashed. A greedy business organization called the Trade Federation created an army and began to invade planets, starting with a small world called Naboo. As the conflict grew, the Republic later deployed its own army. With the galaxy at war, both sides learned too late that they had been manipulated by a deadly Sith Lord!

Sith Lord
The Sith have deadly evil powers. The Sith Lord Darth Sidious plots to destroy the Jedi and rule the entire galaxy.

Warmongers
The Trade Federation and other greedy business corporations take orders from the Sith and use their droid armies to attack the Republic.

Dark forces
The evil Sith Lord Darth Sidious, also known as Emperor Palpatine, peers from his black cape. He is flanked by his trusted servant, Darth Vader, his red-caped guards, and battalions of white-armored stormtroopers.

The Sith were the greediest beings in the galaxy. The leader was called Darth Sidious and he was secretly controlling the Trade Federation. He wanted it to start a war that would put him in power as Emperor. He fooled everyone by pretending to be a kindly politician called Senator Palpatine. Palpatine became leader of the Senate, took control of the Republic's army, and forced every planet to obey him.

Hired hands
Sith Lords often
hire assassins,
spies, and
bounty hunters
to do their dirty
work for them.
Bounty hunters
are skilled
hunters who
kidnap people
for a fee.

A few brave people refused to
accept Palpatine's evil Empire. They
were called the Rebel Alliance—and
they set out to free the galaxy.

This is the story of the Emperor's
rise to power and his downfall at the
hands of the brave-
hearted Rebels. It is a
story of great struggles
on land and in space.
From all-out attacks to
deadly duels and fights
with savage beasts,
these battles are epic!

Rebels at the ready
Luke Skywalker, his twin sister
Princess Leia, Han Solo, and
the Wookiee Chewbacca all
fight for the Rebel Alliance.

Legendary land battles

The galaxy first erupted into violence when the Trade Federation invaded Naboo. This peaceful planet was home to the Naboo people and a water-dwelling species called the Gungans. Two Jedi were sent to investigate: Qui-Gon Jinn and Obi-Wan Kenobi. With help from the Gungans, the Jedi rescued the Naboo Queen, Padmé Amidala.

Vile leaders
The Trade Federation's cowardly leaders land on Naboo only after their battle droids have captured the royal palace.

The Jedi took Queen Amidala to Coruscant to ask the Senate for its help. But the Senate was all talk and no action. Amidala would have to free her planet herself!

She and the Jedi returned to Naboo and battled their way to the hangar where their spaceships were housed. Then Amidala led an attack on the royal palace, fighting many battle droids. Elsewhere, the Gungans fought a battle-droid army. Now the Naboo pilots had to destroy the Trade Federation ship that was controlling the battle droids.

Swift strike
Qui-Gon slices a deadly battle droid in two as he helps Queen Amidala escape from her planet.

Back-up droid
Droideka are even more deadly than battle droids. They carry twin blaster weapons.

Return to Naboo
Qui-Gon Jinn and Obi-Wan Kenobi lead the attempt to recapture Queen Amidala's palace.

Gungan soldiers face the might of the Trade Federation's droid army.

Boss Nass
Queen Amidala asks the Gungan ruler, Boss Nass, to help her fight the invaders.

The deadly land battle between the Gungan army and the massed ranks of battle droids took place on a wide-open grassy plain. At first the Gungans were very clever. They activated special machines carried by their giant swamp lizards. These machines generated an energy bubble that protected the Gungan army from high-speed airborne missiles.

But the Gungans did not realize that battle droids could walk right through their shield. Now the two armies battled each other inside the shield. The Gungans fought bravely but could not hope to win against an endless supply of battle droids. It would take a space battle above Naboo to shut down the droid army.

Binoculars

Atlatl

Electropole

War weapons
Gungans use a variety of unusual weapons that fire balls of explosive energy called plasma. They hurl these balls into the air with catapults and throwing sticks called atlatls.

Energy shields
Gungan soldiers carry glowing energy shields into battle to protect themselves from blaster bolts fired by battle droids.

New leader
The Neimoidian leaders are joined by a powerful new ally, the former Jedi, Count Dooku.

Wheel droids
Sinister hailfire droids roll into battle on giant hoop wheels, while Republic gunships prepare to strike from above.

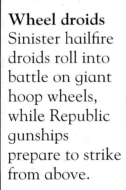

After the Republic learned that its enemies were creating huge droid armies, it was tricked into using a ready-made army to defend itself. Its Army consisted of millions of clone troopers—each clone was an identical copy of a single ultimate soldier. This hastily assembled army first saw action on a planet called Geonosis.

Jedi generals
At the battle of Geonosis, Yoda and many other Jedi have to become military generals for the first time.

Advance guard
Clone troopers blast their way toward the enemy, using special sight systems in their helmets to see through the dense smoke on the battlefield.

The droid armies attacked the Jedi in a large arena on Geonosis. When clone troopers joined the fray, led by Jedi Master Yoda, the battle spread outside the arena. Many Jedi and clone troopers were killed, but finally the droids and their masters retreated. This was the first battle of the famous Clone Wars.

Tarfful
One of the Wookiee leaders is called Tarfful. When the Republic's clone troopers, wheeled tanks, and walking guns go into battle against the droids, Tarfful and the Wookiees are right alongside them.

Droid armies attacked everywhere. One of the biggest battles took place on Kashyyyk. This planet was home to tall, furry creatures called Wookiees. The Wookiees and the Republic army fought on land and sea. But just as victory was in sight, it all went wrong. The Republic did not know that their clone troopers had been brainwashed to switch sides when they received a special signal.

Tanks roll in
On Kashyyyk, many Trade Federation tanks roll over land and water with battle droids mounted on the sides.

When the clones received the signal, Order 66, they turned their weapons on their Jedi generals. The clones took orders only from the Sith. When Darth Sidious became Emperor, the clone troopers became his personal army, known now as stormtroopers. The Empire was born.

Assassination
When the Sith signal is received, every clone commander turns on the Jedi. Nearly all the Jedi leaders are killed. Aayla Secura is assassinated while fighting on the fungi planet, Felucia.

Walking tanks
The Empire's terrifying walking tanks, called AT-ATs, advance across the snow toward the Rebel base.

Great land battles took place in the time of the Empire, too. Many brave individuals joined the Rebel Alliance and fought against the Empire, though they had few weapons, vehicles, or other resources. The Emperor and Darth Vader put much of the Empire's military might toward crushing the Rebel Alliance.

Front line
The Rebels try to hold off the advancing AT-ATs with their heavy guns.

Rebel hangar
The Rebel base is a converted ice cave, with a massive hangar for vehicles.

Darth Vader discovered that the Rebels had built a secret base on the ice planet Hoth. His troops attacked it with great force. He sent in giant walking tanks called AT-ATs. The Rebels tried to hold off the AT-ATs for as long as they could, and even managed to destroy two of them. But eventually they were forced to flee and find another hiding place.

Enter Vader
Sith Lord Darth Vader enters the Rebel base, which is now a smoking ruin. He is flanked by stormtroopers equipped for missions in sub-zero conditions.

Scout trooper
Imperial scout troopers on flying speeder bikes chase down the Rebels when they land on Endor.

After the defeat at Hoth, the Rebels hid all over the galaxy. Palpatine hatched a plan to draw them out. He had once built a huge super-weapon called the Death Star, which the Rebels had destroyed. Now he built a second Death Star, knowing the Rebels would try to stop him. Then he would blow the Rebel fleet out of the sky.

Battle in the forest
Stormtroopers, backed up by a walking AT-ST cannon, do battle with Han and Chewbacca.

The Death Star was protected by a shield generator on the forest moon of Endor. A team of Rebels led by Luke Skywalker, Princess Leia, Han Solo, and Chewbacca went to Endor to destroy the generator. The Rebels faced a large Imperial army, but they were helped by natives called Ewoks. Together they suceeded in destroying the shield generator, and then the Rebel fleet was able to attack the Death Star.

Ewok attack
Small, determined Ewoks hurl rocks at stormtroopers in their well-planned attacks.

Rebel team
Han tries to break into the generator bunker while Leia holds off advancing stormtroopers.

Space battles

Many of the biggest battles in the galaxy took place in space. When the Trade Federation invaded Naboo, its massive battleships surrounded the planet. While the conflict raged on the ground, a handful of Naboo ships managed to take off and fly toward the battleships.

Feared fleet
Deadly Trade Federation vulture droid ships emerge from the ring-shaped Droid Control Ship.

Rookie pilot
Anakin is whisked into the space battle when the autopilot engages in the starfighter he is hiding in.

One of the Naboo
ships was flown—at
first, accidentally— by
a nine-year-old boy
called Anakin
Skywalker. Anakin
had Jedi abilities and

was a superb pilot, although he had
never flown a starship before.
He managed to enter the Trade
Federation's Droid Control Ship and
fire torpedoes into its reactor room,
escaping in his starfighter as
the ship exploded.
Anakin's incredible feat
saved Naboo.

Brave strike
Starfighters
avoid deadly
laser blasts.

Blown away
The Control
Ship sends
instructions to
every battle
droid. When it
is destroyed,
the droids
stop fighting.

Close combat
A Naboo
starfighter
narrowly
avoids a direct
hit as the Droid
Control Ship
fires at oncoming
Naboo ships.

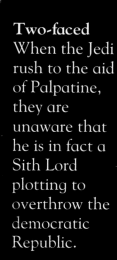

Jedi team
Anakin and Obi-Wan fly side-by-side in their fast Interceptors.

Two-faced
When the Jedi rush to the aid of Palpatine, they are unaware that he is in fact a Sith Lord plotting to overthrow the democratic Republic.

The space battle above Naboo was just the beginning. Worse was yet to come. A full-scale war broke out between the Republic and the droid armies. Their battle fleets met in a gigantic space conflict above Coruscant. The leader of the Republic, Supreme Chancellor Palpatine, had been kidnapped, and two Jedi set off to rescue him: Obi-Wan Kenobi and Anakin Skywalker.

Direct hit
Both sides lose some of their spaceships in the explosive space battle above Coruscant.

The Jedi dodged enemy fire and landed on the cruiser in which Palpatine was being held. After freeing Palpatine, Anakin had to pilot the cruiser to a crash landing after a Republic ship tore it apart.

Tiny but deadly
Small buzz droids attach themselves to the side of Obi-Wan's ship to inflict damage with their cutting arms.

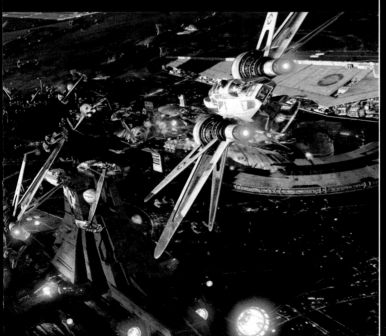

Deadly sky
Republic warships engage droid fighters large and small in the raging battle above Coruscant.

Distinctive ship
Jango pilots one
of the deadliest
ships in the
galaxy, *Slave I*.
It is armed with
weapons and
lethal surprises.

Some space battles involved many ships, like the battle above Coruscant. In others, just two ships engaged in a duel called a dogfight. When Obi-Wan was on the trail of a dangerous villain called Jango Fett, the chase led into a highly lethal asteroid field. Any collision with these floating rocks would be fatal. Jango tried to lose Obi-Wan by blasting rocks close to the Jedi's ship.

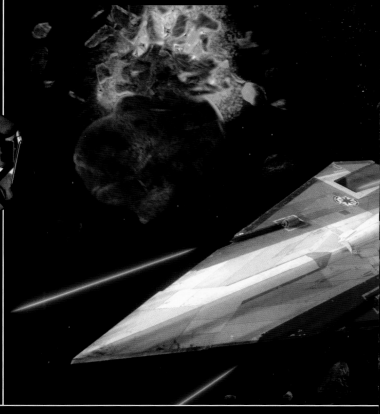

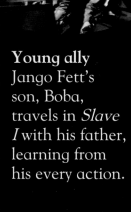

Young ally
Jango Fett's
son, Boba,
travels in *Slave
I* with his father,
learning from
his every action.

Obi-Wan was a skilled pilot and he
dodged each explosion. Then
Jango steered his ship around an
asteroid so he was now the one
pursuing Obi-Wan. He fired a
special seeker missile, but Obi-Wan
faked his ship's explosion. When
Jango saw the blast, he believed that
Obi-Wan had been killed, but the
clever Jedi was really hiding on one
of the asteroids.

On the tail
Seeker missiles
can home in on
fast-moving
objects so they
are hard to
shake off.

Jedi pilot
Even though
Obi-Wan says
he is not keen
on flying, his
piloting skills
are superb.

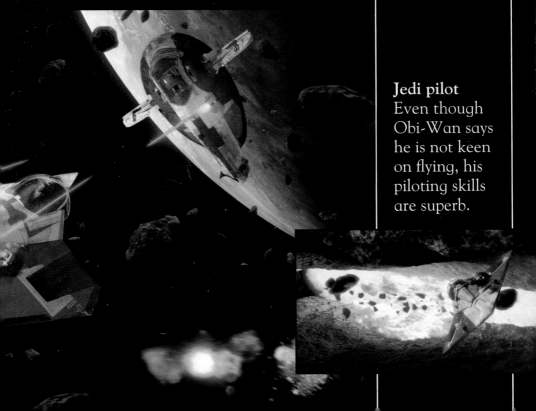

Trusty ship
The *Falcon* is battle scarred from its many space adventures.

Another ship that has been in many dogfights is the *Millennium Falcon*. Piloted by Han Solo and Chewbacca, the ship could outrun most enemy craft. If the going got tough, the *Falcon* could jump to lightspeed, enabling it to vanish instantly and reappear somewhere far away.

Under pressure
A giant Star Destroyer chases the *Falcon* while Imperial TIE-fighters blast it with laser fire.

Han Solo flew the *Falcon* in many daring raids against the Imperial fleet. Once, he landed right on the hull of an enormous Imperial Star Destroyer to evade its radar. Another time, he made the seemingly suicidal decision to fly into an asteroid field to shake off Imperial fighters. The daring plan worked and he escaped with his life.

Heat of battle
Piloted by Han's old friend and rival, Lando Calrissian, the *Falcon* evades Imperial fighters at the second Death Star.

Hot shot
Han Solo was once a reckless smuggler. Then he joined the Rebel Alliance and eventually he even married Princess Leia.

Death Star
The moon-sized Death Star had the firepower to destroy an entire planet.

Strike force
Rebel teams of X-wing and Y-wing starfighter pilots fly from their base on Yavin 4 toward the Death Star.

Rebel space battles

The Rebel Alliance was dedicated to opposing the oppressive rule of the Empire, despite being desperately under-equipped. The Empire had a massive starfleet, but the Alliance made do with a small number of battle-worn starfighters.

The Alliance learned that the Empire had built an enormous battle station called the Death Star. Stolen plans showed a flaw: If a Rebel starfighter could fire a torpedo into a tiny exhaust port, the chain reaction would destroy the battle station.

Rebel pilot
Luke stays calm and focused in his starfighter spaceship as he leads the attack on the Death Star.

The Rebel pilots boldly launched an assault on the Death Star from their base on the planet Yavin 4. The Empire was not expecting an attack on its deadly superweapon. One Rebel pilot was skilled enough to strike the target: Luke Skywalker. The Death Star exploded—and the Rebels scored their first major victory against the Empire.

Enemy ships
Two Imperial ships chase the Rebel pilots along a narrow trench on the Death Star.

Hot shot
Luke hits the exhaust port that leads into the heart of the battle station's colossal reactor.

Rebel leader
Admiral Ackbar is the loyal Commander of the Rebel fleet at the Battle of Endor.

The battle rages around the half-completed Death Star.

The Battle of Endor was the final showdown between the Rebels and the Empire. Part of the conflict took place above the forest moon of Endor, where the Empire was building a second Death Star. While a team of Rebels landed on Endor's moon to disable the shield generator protecting the Death Star, the entire Rebel fleet came out of hiding to launch a final, do-or-die attack.

A Rebel ship crashes into the bridge of an Imperial Star Destroyer, while Rebel B-wings fly in formation nearby.

At one point in the battle, Rebels targeted the Empire's Star Destroyers, hoping the Death Star would hold fire to avoid hitting its own ships. The battle turned when a damaged Rebel ship crashed into a Super Star Destroyer. With the shield down, Rebel ships could attack the Death Star's power plant, causing a fatal explosion.

Direct assault
The *Millennium Falcon* flew through the Death Star's superstructure to detonate the battle station's power plant.

Lightsaber clashes

Since ancient times, the lightsaber has been the chosen weapon of the Jedi Knights. Until the Sith emerged from hiding, the Jedi used their lightsabers only as defence against blasters and other weapons. But the Sith also used lightsabers. Now the Jedi faced opponents armed with their own traditional weapon.

Surprise attack
Darth Maul first appears on the desert planet Tatooine. He ambushes Jedi Qui-Gon Jinn.

Sith opponent
On Naboo, it takes two skilled Jedi to hold back Darth Maul's double-bladed lightsaber.

*Obi-Wan leaps to avoid a low
parry from Maul's glowing blade.*

During the Battle of Naboo,
Darth Sidious's Sith apprentice,
Darth Maul, emerged. Maul's
appearance was terrifying, with face
tattoos, yellow eyes, and several
horns. Darth Maul attacked Jedi
Qui-Gon Jinn and Obi-Wan Kenobi.
He managed to kill Qui-Gon. Obi-
Wan was devastated but he fought
on until he had defeated his Sith foe.

Jedi in trouble
On the edge of
a deep shaft,
Maul nearly
triumphs over
Obi-Wan. But
the Jedi will not
give up until he
has defeated the
savage Sith.

Sith blade
Dooku's lightsaber blade is red, as all Sith blades are.

Captured Jedi
On Geonosis, Count Dooku wants Obi-Wan Kenobi to join him as a Sith.

With Darth Maul dead, Sith Lord Darth Sidious had to train a new apprentice. He chose a former Jedi called Count Dooku. The elegant, commanding Dooku left the Jedi Order to become a Sith. Sidious taught him to use the destructive dark side of the Force.

At the Battle of Geonosis, Dooku fought a great Jedi Master, Yoda. They clashed in a blur of lightsaber blows. Dooku used the Force to throw massive objects. This time, he managed to escape.

Jedi against Sith
The Jedi fight Dooku
onboard the cruiser.

Dooku next
faced Obi-Wan
and Anakin on
the cruiser where
Palpatine (really Darth
Sidious) was being held prisoner.
Dooku knocked Obi-Wan
unconscious. But he was unaware of
Sidious's masterplan: He wanted
Anakin to kill Dooku and replace
him as his new Sith apprentice.

Bad influence
Palpatine
encourages
Anakin to reject
his Jedi training
and unleash his
anger to kill
Dooku in
cold blood.

Count Dooku was not the only lightsaber-wielding foe the Jedi would meet during the Clone Wars. They also confronted a half-machine, half-living creature called Grievous, who was general of the droid armies. Grievous had also been trained by Count Dooku in lightsaber combat. He liked to steal lightsabers from the Jedi he killed, and hoped to add Obi-Wan and Anakin's weapons to his collection.

Lethal general
On Utapau, Obi-Wan finds that General Grievous is a dangerous opponent in lightsaber combat.

Utapau chase
Grievous on his wheelbike and Obi-Wan on a fast varactyl lizard trade blows on the planet Utapau.

Furious foe
Grievous's two arms can split into four, giving the Jedi extra lightsabers to dodge and parry. Obi-Wan will shear off some of these extra limbs.

But not this time! The daring Jedi fought off Grievous's bodyguards and escaped the general's clutches.

Grievous next met Obi-Wan on the planet Utapau. Wielding four lightsabers, Grievous unleashed a brutal assault. A high-speed chase across the planet surface led to a final showdown—and Grievous's dramatic demise in a ball of fire.

Explosive end
Obi-Wan uses a blaster to fire the fatal shots that enflame Grievous.

Lost cause
On the volcano planet called Mustafar, Obi-Wan realizes that Anakin is no longer a Jedi.

Sith opponent
Anakin, now named Darth Vader, unleashes his Sith powers against Obi-Wan Kenobi.

Ever since Senator Palpatine first met Anakin Skywalker, he knew the young Jedi had great powers. He also perceived Anakin's unruly emotions and knew he could be turned to the Sith cause. After he had encouraged Anakin to kill Dooku, Palpatine revealed that he was a Sith, and Anakin joined him, becoming Darth Vader. Then Palpatine made Vader believe Obi-Wan was against him.

Anakin's eyes gleam with anger as Obi-Wan defeats him in battle.

Darth Vader and Obi-Wan fought on the volcano planet Mustafar. Obi-Wan gained the upper hand and left Vader for dead. But Emperor Palpatine rebuilt Vader in black armor. Then Vader took his place beside the Emperor.

Darth Vader fought Obi-Wan once more, taking the Jedi's life. It wasn't until he battled with his own son that Vader was able to reject the Sith and the dark side.

Deadly rematch
Vader and Obi-Wan meet in combat for the last time on the first Death Star.

Father-son duel
Vader wants his son Luke to join him as a Sith, but Luke refused.

Cruel Master
Palpatine enjoys the fight between his Sith accomplice, Dooku, and his accomplice-to-be, Anakin.

Sith unmasked
Palpatine displays his Sith lightsaber skills in the fight with Mace Windu.

For a long time, the most evil Sith Lord in the galaxy went by the name of Palpatine. Pretending to be a friend to the Republic, he secretly masterminded a war that made him the cruel ruler of the galaxy.

The Jedi realized too late that Palpatine was really a Sith Lord named Darth Sidious. High-ranking Jedi Master Mace Windu lost his life attempting to stop the Sith schemer.

Palpatine had hidden his Sith lightsaber until Mace confronted him.

Even Yoda was unable to defeat the Emperor in lightsaber combat. In the end, Sidious's own ally, Darth Vader, sided with Vader's son, Luke Skywalker. Vader turned against his Sith Master and threw Emperor Palpatine to his death.

Explosive clash
The two most powerful users of the Force's light and dark sides clash in a spectacular duel in the Senate building on Coruscant.

Lightning strike
Sidious fires deadly Sith lightning at Luke. But Vader will be unable to stand by and let his son die.

Famous showdowns

Jango finds that Obi-Wan is hard to hit with a blaster.

Airborne foe
Jango uses his jetpack to soar above Obi-Wan on Kamino.

Final end
In the arena battle on Geonosis, Jedi Mace Windu strikes the fatal blow that ends Jango's life.

Even before the Clone Wars, the galaxy was not entirely peaceful. Many criminals thrived, including bounty hunters, who captured or attacked people for a price. The best bounty hunter in the galaxy was named Jango Fett. Jango wore sleek armor and carried many weapons. He clashed with Obi-Wan on a watery planet called Kamino.

Though Jango escaped, the Battle of Geonosis would be his undoing. In the combat, Mace Windu struck Jango down with a powerful thrust from his lightsaber blade.

Jango's son Boba witnessed his father's death. Boba became a bounty hunter like his father. He came to work for Darth Vader and the notorious gangster Jabba the Hutt, among others. With Vader's help, Boba captured Han Solo and delivererd him to Jabba, who wanted Han for unpaid debts. A fierce battle ensued when Luke Skywalker and his friends rescued Solo from Jabba.

Battle-scarred
Boba Fett had many famous showdowns in his career as a bounty hunter. But he meets his match in the battle at Jabba's palace.

Deadly duel
Boba clashes with Luke, but a lucky strike from Han will knock the bounty hunter out of the battle.

Enter the beast
The three-horned reek enters the arena on Geonosis for a showdown with the human prisoners.

Jedi Knights, Rebels, and other defenders of freedom in the galaxy have had many showdowns with bounty hunters, assassins, and vile gangsters. They have also faced some nightmarish beasts.

On the planet Geonosis, Obi-Wan, Anakin, and Padmé Amidala were sentenced to public execution—by savage beasts.

Bared teeth
A soldier prods the nexu into the arena with a spear, where it bears its fangs in anticipation of fresh meat.

Obi-Wan faces the fearsome acklay in the Geonosis arena.

The blood-thirsty
acklay walked on three
pairs of giant claws. The reek
had three pointed horns on its
head for goring opponents. The
nexu had a mouthful of sharp teeth.
Obi-Wan managed to fell the acklay
with his lightsaber blade. Anakin
jumped on top of the reek and
charged it into the nexu.

Rancor beast
In Jabba's
palace, a caged
beast called a
rancor is let
loose upon Luke
Skywalker, but
proves no match
for the new Jedi.

Jabba's death
The massive
slug-like
gangster Jabba
the Hutt meets
an untimely end
at the hands of
Princess Leia.

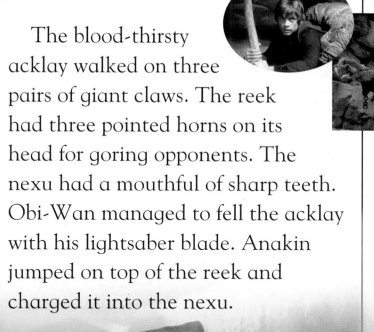

A new era

At last—victory for the Rebel Alliance! The deaths of Emperor Palpatine and Darth Vader, and the destruction of the second Death Star, meant that the Empire was doomed. Peace and justice would soon be restored to the galaxy. The good news spread quickly and people rejoiced.

Father and son reunited
Luke looks at his father's true face for the first time, revealed beneath Darth Vader's helmet.

Forest celebration
In Endor's forests, Rebels and Ewoks celebrate the destruction of the terrible second Death Star that had threatened all of their lives.

The Rebel Alliance established a New Republic to replace the Empire. But troubles continued. Hundreds of planets that had accepted the Emperor's rule needed to be won over. Many loyal Imperial officers continued to attack the New Republic with remnants of the Imperial fleet. For Luke Skywalker, Han Solo, Princess Leia, and their allies, a new era had begun but the epic battle was not over yet.

Good times
Above the gigantic skyscrapers on Coruscant, fireworks light up the skies in celebration of the defeat of the evil Empire.

Glossary

Alien
A creature from outer space.

Apprentice
A person who is learning a skill.

Asteroid
A rock that floats in space.

Blaster
A gun that fires a deadly beam of light.

Clone
An exact copy of another person.

Dark side
The part of the Force associated with hatred.

Death Star
A moon-sized superweapon developed by the Empire.

Emperor
The leader of an Empire is called an Emperor. Palpatine is the Emperor who rules the Galactic Empire.

Empire
A group of peoples ruled by one leader.

The Force
An energy field created by all living things.

Force lightning
A Sith power, which involves firing deadly electricity from fingertips.

Galaxy
A group of millions of stars and planets.

Jedi Knight
A *Star Wars* warrior with special powers who defends the good of the galaxy.

Jedi Master
A high-ranking Jedi who has exceptional skills in using the Force.

Jedi Order
The name of the group that defends peace and justice in the galaxy.

Lightsaber
A Jedi's or Sith's sword-like weapon, with a blade of glowing energy.

Light side
The part of the Force associated with goodness, compassion, and healing

Lightspeed
A special kind of travel that allows a spaceship to cross vast distances of space in an instant.

Parry
To ward off a strike from a lightsaber or other sword-like weapon.

Reactor
A device in spaceships used to generate power for travel.

Rebel
Someone who opposes their government or ruler.

Republic
A nation or group of nations in which the people vote for their leaders.

Senate
The governing body of the Republic.

Senator
A member of the Senate. He or she will have been chosen (elected) by the people of his or her country.

Shield
An invisible protective barrier around a spaceship, planet, or other object.

Sith
Enemies of the Jedi who use the dark side of the Force.

STAR WARS™
BEWARE THE
DARK SIDE

Written by Simon Beecroft

Faces of Evil

A long time ago, the galaxy was ruled by an evil man named Darth Sidious (pronounced SID-EE-US). He was also known as Emperor Palpatine (pronounced PAL-PA-TEEN). He used fear, corruption, and the dark side of the Force to rule his evil Empire.

The Force
The Force is an invisible energy created by all living things. A few people with special powers can control the Force. The Force is mostly a good energy, but it also has a dark side that can be used for evil.

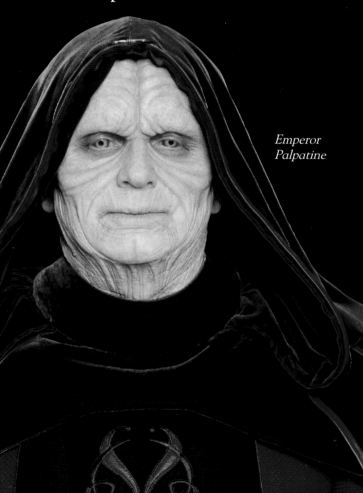

Emperor Palpatine

Darth Sidious's special abilities made him very powerful. He used the dark side of the Force to control people's minds and events. He also used the dark side to throw heavy objects with his mind, and to fire a deadly lightning from his fingers.

In these pages, you will meet many villains who used the dark side of the Force to do terrible things. You will also meet evildoers who did not use the Force, but who were still on the side of darkness. Finally, you will meet the brave few who dared to stand up to the dark side.

The Jedi order
Jedi Master Obi-Wan Kenobi said that the Force "surrounds us, penetrates us, and binds the galaxy together". The Jedi are a group of individuals who devote their lives to using the Force for good. The Jedi protect people and keep peace in the galaxy.

Sith lightsabers
Each Jedi builds his or her own weapon called a lightsaber. They are made from glowing energy crystals. Sith lightsaber blades are usually red.

Sith Lord

Darth Sidious was a Sith Lord. The Sith had been around for many centuries. The first Sith was a Jedi who turned to the dark side. Others followed him. Together they tried to destroy the Jedi. The Sith even tried to kill each other because they were so full of evil and hatred. The Jedi thought they had destroyed the Sith. But, one Sith survived. He took an apprentice and went into hiding. Since then, the Sith have plotted revenge on the Jedi.

The Sith were the Jedi's most feared enemies. The Sith used the dark side of the Force to gain terrible powers. Like the Jedi, they fought with a lightsaber, which is a sword whose blade is made of pure energy. The Sith and the Jedi were the only people in the galaxy who used lightsabers. The lightsaber was the ancient weapon of the Jedi, but since the Sith were once Jedi, they used them too.

Lightsabers
The handle contains special crystals that make the energy blade appear when needed. Jedi lightsaber blades are either blue, green, or purple.

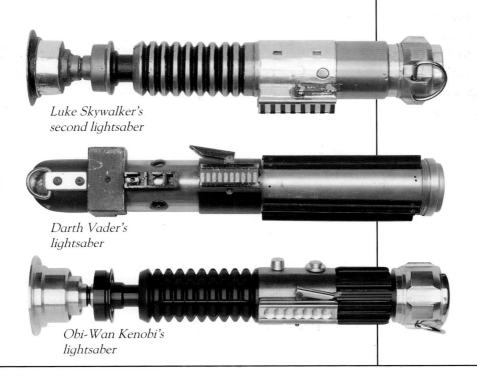

Luke Skywalker's second lightsaber

Darth Vader's lightsaber

Obi-Wan Kenobi's lightsaber

Sith Powers

The Sith believed that the dark side of the Force was more powerful than the light. Turning to the dark side seemed to bring results quickly, while the Jedi had to patiently study the light side of the Force for many years. The Sith also rejected the Jedi's teachings that emotions must be controlled. They used anger and hatred to become stronger, but the Sith had no loyalty and were often destroyed by the dark side.

Evil temptation
The Jedi understood that the dark side was a powerful temptation for all Jedi. Most managed to resist it, but a few gave in to its evil powers.

In battle, the Sith tried to crush their opponents with heavy objects, which they threw using their dark side energies.

The dark side of the Force gave the Sith powers that the Jedi did not have. One of them was deadly Force lightning. They could fire it from their fingers at an opponent. However, this power was very dangerous and could also harm the user.

Force lightning
When Sidious attacked a Jedi called Mace Windu with Force lightning, Mace threw it back at Sidious. The lightning hit Sidious's face and scarred it forever.

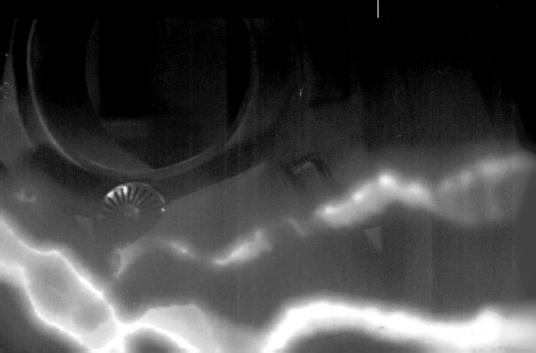

Galactic Republic

When the galaxy was united in peace, a Galactic Republic was formed. It was a democracy, which meant that every person in nearly all the worlds had a voice.

The Phantom Menace

Before Darth Sidious became Emperor of the galaxy, he was a popular politician called Senator Palpatine. At this time, the galaxy was at peace and laws were made in the Senate. All the different planets had a voice in the Senate and large armies were outlawed.

Palpatine secretly wanted to take over the galaxy. He planned to destroy the Senate and build a massive army so that he could force every planet to do what he wanted.

No one suspected that Palpatine was really a Sith Lord. After he secretly started a war in the galaxy, Palpatine convinced the Senate to make him their leader, the Supreme Chancellor. Then he gave himself the power to make all the decisions. Finally, he crowned himself Emperor. Now the dark side ruled the galaxy.

The Senate
The Senate was a gigantic circular building on the galaxy's capital planet, Coruscant.

Secret Sith
Palpatine hid his true Sith identity from the Senate.

Jedi Defenders

When the Sith revealed themselves after two thousand years in hiding, only the Jedi had the powers to face them. The Jedi vow to use their Force powers only to do good. The good side of the Force is known as the light side.

Learning to use the light side of the Force takes many years. Those who become Jedi begin training as young children. They must leave their families behind and live in the Jedi Temple on a big planet.

Yoda
Yoda was the wisest Jedi of all. He was hundreds of years old when the Sith reappeared.

The Jedi learn to control their emotions so that they can remain calm and practical in all situations. The Jedi seek to keep the Force in balance in the galaxy, which means that they must stop those who seek to use the dark side.

The Jedi can actually listen to the Force telling them that there is trouble happening somewhere. This is known as a disturbance in the Force. It means there's a problem some place in the galaxy— and the Jedi must find it and do whatever they can to stop it.

Obi-Wan
Obi-Wan Kenobi was a powerful Jedi. While the Sith ruled the galaxy, Obi-Wan went into hiding. Yoda also went into hiding.

Jedi Council
The wisest, most experienced Jedi sat on the Jedi High Council. Before the Sith attacked, Yoda felt great disturbances in the Force, but even he was not able to see where the threat came from.

Masked man
Vader's armor and breathing equipment were created in a secret medical facility.

Vader uncovered
Vader removed his helmet only in a special isolation chamber. Mechanical arms lifted the helmet from his scarred head.

Darth Vader

Darth Vader ruled the galaxy alongside Darth Sidious. Vader was also a Sith Lord. His knowledge of the dark side of the Force made him a powerful and dangerous figure. Vader would kill anyone who got in his way or disobeyed him, even his own generals. He used his Force powers to strangle people without even touching them.

Darth Vader always
wore a black suit of
armor and a black
mask because his body
had been almost
destroyed in a great
battle. His armor and mask
contained breathing equipment and
life-support systems to keep him
alive. The wheezing sound of
Vader's artificial breathing was
enough to strike terror into the mind
of anyone he approached.

Space fighter
Vader flew his
own fighter ship
into combat.
He was a very
daring pilot.

Lightsaber duel
Vader was a
merciless
opponent in
battle, and did
not hesitate to
cut down his
former Master,
Obi-Wan
Kenobi.

Anakin Skywalker

Boyhood
Anakin was born on a poor desert planet called Tatooine. He spent his boyhood as a slave until a Jedi Master named Qui-Gon Jinn rescued him.

Tragic death
When Anakin joined the Jedi, he had to leave his mother behind. He never forgave himself when he could not prevent her from dying at the hands of a vicious species called Sand People.

Before he became a Sith Lord, Darth Vader was a Jedi called Anakin Skywalker. Anakin was one of the most talented Jedi ever. His Force powers were incredibly strong, but Anakin was impatient.

He wanted to become more powerful than any other Jedi.

Palpatine befriended Anakin and began to plant ideas in his mind. He convinced Anakin to join him on the dark side and train to be a Sith. Palpatine told Anakin that the dark side of the Force was more powerful than the light side. He even told Anakin that he would be able to stop his wife from dying. Anakin wanted this more than anything, so he rejected his Jedi training and joined Palpatine.

When Anakin joined the dark side, he killed many Jedi. He even fought his best friend, Obi-Wan Kenobi. On the edge of a lava river, Anakin and Obi-Wan fought fiercely until Obi-Wan managed to strike down his former friend. Anakin fell near the red-hot lava and burst into flames. Palpatine rescued him, and re-built his badly burned body with robotic parts and a suit of armor—and Darth Vader was born!

Padmé Amidala
Anakin secretly married the Senator for Naboo, Padmé Amidala, even though the Jedi are forbidden to marry.

Maul

Each Sith Master chose a single apprentice, whom he trained in the dark side. Sidious first chose a savage alien from the planet Iridonia. Given the Sith name Darth Maul, he served his master obediently, although he was only waiting for the day when he would take Sidious's place. Maul had horns on his head and yellow eyes. His face was tattooed with dark side symbols. Maul's weapon was a double-bladed lightsaber.

Sith ship
Maul's spaceship could make itself appear invisible to others.

Speeder
Maul also used a speeder that flew along just above the ground. It had an open cockpit.

158

When two Jedi named Qui-Gon Jinn (pronounced KWY-GONN-JIN) and Obi-Wan Kenobi (pronounced OH-BEE-ONE KEN-OH-BEE) started to upset Sidious's plans, he sent Maul to kill them. The fight took place on the edge of a giant power generator on Palpatine's home planet, Naboo. The Jedi were not prepared for such a ferocious attack. Qui-Gon was killed, but Obi-Wan defeated the deadly Sith apprentice.

Sith Master
Sidious kept in contact with his apprentice using a hologram transmitter.

Count Dooku

Sidious needed a new apprentice after Obi-Wan killed Darth Maul on Naboo. His search led him to Count Dooku, who was once a Jedi Master. Although he joined the Jedi order at a young age, Dooku was interested in the dark side and wanted power to change things quickly. When Dooku joined Sidious, he took the new Sith name—
Darth Tyranus.

Weapon
Tyranus's weapon was a lightsaber with a curved handle. His special moves could surprise even the most experienced Jedi.

Count Dooku

For many years, Dooku had been encouraging planets and business organizations to leave the Senate and build droid

armies. He told them that this would make the galaxy a better place. In reality he was doing only what Sidious told him to do. He did not know what Sidious's true plans were.

Sidious eventually betrayed Dooku and allowed him to be killed by Anakin Skywalker. Sidious knew that the powerful and gifted Anakin would be a more useful Sith apprentice than Dooku.

Force lightning
Like Sidious, Tyranus used Force lightning to deadly effect.

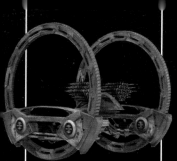

Droid Army

Count Dooku had persuaded many planets and organizations to buy powerful droid armies. The footsoldiers were blaster-wielding battle droids while heavily armored super battle droids provided backup. Hailfire droids rolled across the battlefields, each equipped with deadly cannon or missile launchers. Deadly machines called droideka were used on special missions.

Hailfire droids
Hailfire droids are shaped like massive wheels. They can race across flat ground or shallow lakes, flattening anything in their path.

Tri-fighter
Tri-fighters seek out and hunt down enemy ships in space, training their deadly nose cannons on their prey.

Heavily armed droid ships were also used for space battles. They included vulture droids, which could also walk along the ground, and tri-fighters. Swarms of tiny buzz droids attached themselves to enemy ships. Although they were very small, their cutting and sawing arms could inflict serious damage.

Spider droids
Spider droids go into battle equipped with heat-seeking missiles.

General Grievous

With the outbreak of war in the galaxy, many brutal fiends joined the Sith Lords. One such recruit was General Grievous, a warlord whose battle-scarred body had been rebuilt with cyborg parts. The only parts of his original body left were his reptile-like eyes and his inner organs, which were protected by armor. Although he was more machine than man, Grievous would kill anyone who called him a droid.

Bodyguards
Grievous was accompanied by droid bodyguards, who were equipped with deadly energy staffs.

Grievous became Supreme Commander of the droid armies. Dooku taught Grievous to use a lightsaber, although Grievous could not use the Force like the Sith and Jedi.

Grievous had a long-standing grudge against the Jedi, and took the lightsabers of any Jedi he killed. In battle, Grievous could split his two arms into four, each of which could wield a lightsaber. He also used a deadly blaster and a powerful energy staff, which delivered fatal electric shocks to his opponents.

Final battle
Grievous was no match for the combined power of the Jedi Obi-Wan Kenobi and Anakin Skywalker.

Clone Soldiers

Although Sidious had started a war in the galaxy, he didn't want either side to win it. He wanted the war to go on just long enough for him to bring the Sith to power. He made sure that the Republic had an army of its own, so that each side was evenly matched. The Republic army consisted of well-trained clone soldiers and a variety of battle tanks, plus cannons, gunships, and space assault ships.

Special training
Each clone trooper was an identical copy of a single "supreme soldier" named Jango Fett. Each clone was grown in a factory and trained for combat from birth.

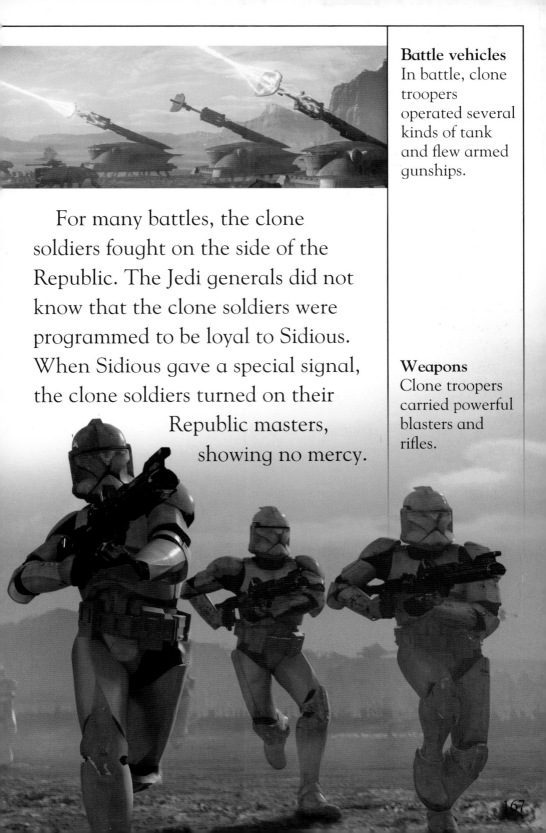

Battle vehicles
In battle, clone troopers operated several kinds of tank and flew armed gunships.

For many battles, the clone soldiers fought on the side of the Republic. The Jedi generals did not know that the clone soldiers were programmed to be loyal to Sidious. When Sidious gave a special signal, the clone soldiers turned on their Republic masters, showing no mercy.

Weapons
Clone troopers carried powerful blasters and rifles.

167

Stormtroopers

When the war was over, Darth Sidious ruled the galaxy as Emperor Palpatine, and the clone soldiers became his personal army. He renamed them stormtroopers and forced many millions of human males to join their ranks. Military Academies were formed in which new recruits were trained to be foot soldiers or more specialized troops, such as pilots or scouts. The stormtroopers were trained to be totally loyal to the Empire.

Armor
Stormtrooper armor protected the soldier inside from weapon and bomb blasts.

Stormtrooper

The stormtroopers could not be bribed or persuaded into betraying the Emperor. People everywhere learned to fear the sinister white-armored troops.

Snowtroopers Some stormtroopers wore specialized armor to protect them from the cold on freezing planets. They were called snowtroopers.

Vader's son
Luke was raised
on Anakin's
home planet,
Tatooine, by his
uncle and aunt.

**Vader's
daughter**
Leia was raised
on the planet
Alderaan. She
became a
Princess—and
a secret member
of the Rebel
Alliance.

Empire and Rebels

When Darth Sidious came to
power, a dark age began in the
galaxy—the Empire. As Emperor
Palpatine, Sidious used his massive
armies to terrify the galaxy and to
stop anyone from rising against him.

Nevertheless, a secret opposition
was formed, called the Rebel
Alliance. The most famous Rebels
were the children of Darth Vader,
Luke and Leia.

When Anakin Skywalker turned to the dark side, he did not know that his wife, Padmé Amidala, was pregnant with twins. Tragically, Padmé died while giving birth. The twins were hidden away in separate places, so that Anakin would not find out about them.

Rebel Alliance
Leia and the Rebel Alliance plan an attack on the Empire from their secret base on the planet Yavin 4.

Han Solo
The Rebels welcomed any support they could get, even from former smugglers like Han Solo and Chewbacca.

Jango Fett

The first clone troopers were cloned from a single "supreme warrior." He was a man named Jango Fett. Jango made his living as a bounty hunter. This means that he was paid to hunt criminals and outlaws. Darth Tyranus knew of his unbeatable combat skills and recruited him for the secret clone-army project.

Warrior upbringing
Jango was an orphan. He was raised by a legendary warrior army, thought to be the most dangerous in the galaxy.

Equipment
Jango wore a protective helmet to hide his identity. A jetpack allowed him to blast into the air and escape.

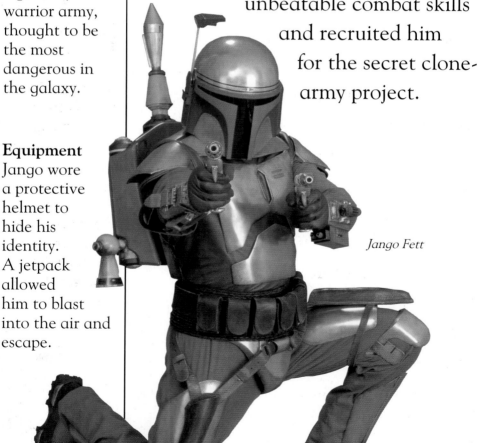

Jango Fett

Jango also carried out certain special missions for the Sith Lords. For example, he would assassinate any public figures that stood between the Sith Lords and their ultimate goal of ruling the galaxy. One such person was the good Senator Padmé Amidala. Thankfully, Padmé survived the attempts on her life, and the Jedi pursued Jango. Eventually, Jango was killed in a large battle between the Republic army and the droid army.

Jetpack
Jango uses his jetpack to attack Jedi Obi-Wan from above.

Flame thrower
Jango fires his deadly wrist-mounted flame thrower.

Airspeeder
When Zam
needed to make
a fast getaway,
she jumped into
her fast, green
airspeeder.

Zam Wesell

Jango Fett had many contacts in
the criminal underworld. One such
contact was the hired assassin Zam
Wesell. Zam was an alien whose
species could shape-shift, which
meant that she could change her
body shape to imitate other species.
This was useful when she needed
to blend in with another planet's
species without being noticed.

Jango hired Zam to carry out the daring murder of the politician Senator Padmé Amidala. First Zam tried to blow up the Senator's spaceship. Then, she released deadly insects called kouhuns into Padmé's bedroom while she slept, but her Jedi bodyguards were able to stop the attack in time. Zam was chased by the Jedi Obi-Wan Kenobi and Anakin Skywalker. They managed to capture her, but before she could give anything away, she was shot by a mysterious figure in the shadows— Jango Fett.

Jedi protector
Obi-Wan was trying to protect Senator Amidala.

True face
When shape-shifters die, they return to their own body shape.

Boba Fett

When Jango Fett was killed in battle, he left a young son named Boba. Young Boba had spent his whole life learning from his father, so when he grew up, he too became a bounty hunter. Boba inherited his father's armor and weapons, and became the best bounty hunter in the galaxy.

Boba often worked for Darth Vader, tracking down enemies of the Empire.

When Darth Vader learned that he had a son, he wanted to track him down and see if he could turn him to the dark side. He would have liked to rule the galaxy alongside his son.

Like father, like son
Boba Fett is an exact, unaltered clone of his father, Jango.

Secret weapons
Boba's armor conceals a deadly flame thrower and powerful rocket dart launchers.

Vader employed Boba Fett
to find and capture Luke,
but Luke was firmly
on the side of
good. He had
begun to train as a
Jedi and refused to
turn to the dark side.

Boba was eventually
defeated during a battle with Luke
Skywalker and his allies. Boba Fett's
jetpack was damaged, causing it to
malfunction. It sent the bounty
hunter soaring into the air, out of
control. Fett finally tumbled to his
death into the ravenous jaws of
a giant desert creature called
the Sarlacc.

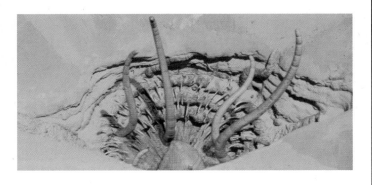

**Armed
spaceship**
Boba traveled in
his father's ship,
"Slave I".
The ship was
full of weapons.

Possible escape
Some people
believe that
Boba managed
to escape from
the stomach of
the Sarlacc.

Criminal Species
Jabba was a Hutt, a species known for its ruthless ways. Hutts ran most of the galaxy's large crime gangs.

Jabba the Hutt

Another of Boba Fett's employers was a crime lord named Jabba the Hutt. This repellent slug-like creature was the leader of a large crime empire responsible for all kinds of shady deals, including murder, theft, and fraud. Jabba lived in a palace on the desert planet Tatooine. He shared his palace with assorted gangsters, assassins, smugglers, corrupt officials, low-life entertainers, and servants.

Jabba paid Boba Fett to bring him a smuggler who owed him money. That smuggler was Han Solo, who had become friends with Luke and Leia Skywalker. When Han was captured and brought to Jabba, Leia set out with Chewbacca to rescue Han. When she was also captured, it was up to Luke to rescue all his friends. During Luke's rescue mission, Leia was able to wrap a chain around Jabba's neck and defeat him.

Bib Fortuna
Bib Fortuna ran Jabba's palace for him. He had a large head tail, sharp teeth, and scary red eyes.

Pet monster
Jabba kept a ferocious rancor monster in a cellar pit. Sometimes he fed it human captives for fun.

Rogues and Villains

Even before the Empire took control, parts of the galaxy were wild and lawless. On remote planets like Tatooine, highly dangerous Podraces were organized, although they were officially banned. Slavery was also common. When the Jedi Qui-Gon visited Tatooine, he met a slave dealer named Watto. Watto owned Anakin Skywalker and his mother, Shmi. Anakin and Shmi both worked for Watto in his junk shop.

Informer
Garindan was a low-life informer who lived on Tatooine.

Watto
Watto made Anakin and Shmi work very hard.

Under the Empire, crime was often rewarded. The Empire relied on spies to report suspicious behavior. Often, it forced officials to do its shady business.

When Darth Vader wanted to capture Luke Skywalker, he threatened to shut down an entire city if its leader, Lando Calrissian, did not lure Luke into a trap. When Vader broke his promise, Lando helped Luke and joined the Rebels.

Calrissian
Lando Calrissian had great charm.

Greedo
Greedo was a small-time hitman hired to kill Han Solo.

Imperial Might

The Empire kept control of the galaxy with its gigantic army of stormtroopers and a fleet of warships that patrolled all the major space routes. The biggest warship was Darth Vader's personal ship, the "Executor." The "Executor" led a fleet of Star Destroyers.

Heavy weapons
Star Destroyers were armed with many powerful weapons.

Each Star Destroyer had enough firepower to destroy entire planets. Swarming around these big ships were countless smaller TIE-fighters, each piloted by a fighter pilot.

When the Empire discovered a Rebel secret base on the ice planet Hoth, it sent in massive walking tanks called AT-ATs. Pilots controlled the tanks from a cockpit in the head. Until the battle of Hoth, AT-ATs were thought to be unbeatable in battle, but the Rebels toppled them by wrapping cables around their legs.

Scout walkers
Smaller AT-ST, or scout walkers, patrolled many planets.

Sinister spy
A probe droid spotted the Rebel base on Hoth and informed the Empire.

Torture
Onboard the
Death Star,
Darth Vader
threatened to
use a torture
droid on
Princess Leia
to make her
reveal the
whereabouts of
the Rebel bases.

Death Star

The Death Star was the Emperor's most terrifying superweapon. It was the size of small moon, but it was actually one of the largest starships ever built. Its gigantic superlaser weapon could destroy entire planets. To demonstrate its enormous power,

the Empire used it to destroy the planet of Alderaan. This was the planet on which Darth Vader's daughter, Leia, had lived most of her life.

Fatal flaw
The unguarded exhaust port was
located at the end of a long channel
on the surface of the Death Star.

Mastermind
One of the
Emperor's
leaders, Grand
Moff Tarkin,
was the
mastermind
behind the
Death Star.

Yet even the Death Star had a
flaw. If a skilled pilot could fire
torpedoes into a small exhaust shaft
on the Death Star's surface, a chain
reaction of explosions would blow up
the entire starship. The Rebel
Alliance sent their best pilots
to reach the target. Luke
Skywalker trusted in
the Force and fired.
A direct hit! Luke
had managed to
destroy the Empire's
most terrible weapon.

Second Death Star
After the Rebels destroyed the first Death Star, Emperor Palpatine ordered that a replacement be built.

Rebel Victory

The brave Rebels refused to give up the fight against Emperor Palpatine and his Empire of evil. Although the Emperor commanded the biggest army in the galaxy, he was not invincible. The Rebels teamed up with a band of forest-dwelling creatures called Ewoks on the planet Endor. Together they overpowered the Emperor's stormtroopers and helped the Rebels' spaceships to launch a full-scale attack on the second Death Star.

Look out!
The Ewoks only used weapons made of wood, yet they managed to defeat the well-trained and well-armed stormtroopers.

Meanwhile onboard the Death Star, Luke battled for his life against the Emperor and Darth Vader. When Luke refused to turn to the dark side, the Emperor forced the father and son to fight. In the end, Luke could not kill Vader and when the Emperor tried to kill Luke, Vader turned against his Sith Master and threw him to his doom down a deep shaft.

Luke had proven that even those who have turned to the dark side still have good inside them that can be reached—if you only know how.

Vader unmasked Luke lifted Vader's mask to gaze at the face of the father he had never known.

Glossary

Apprentice
A person who is learning a skill.

Blaster
A gun that fires a deadly beam of light.

Bounty hunter
A person who hunts criminals and other wanted people, in return for money.

Clone
An exact copy of another person.

Dark side
The part of the Force associated with fear and hatred.

Droid
A kind of robot.

Emperor
The leader of an Empire is called an Emperor. Palpatine is the Emperor who rules the Galactic Empire.

Empire
A group of nations ruled by one leader.

The Force
An energy field created by all living things.

Force lightning
One of the Sith's powers which involved firing deadly electricity from their fingers.

Galactic
Something from or to do with a galaxy.

Galaxy
A group of millions of stars and planets.

Jedi Council
The governing body of the Jedi order. The wisest Jedi, such as Yoda, sit on the Council.

Jedi Knight
A *Star Wars* warrior with special powers who defends the good of the galaxy. Anakin Skywalker, Luke Skywalker, and Ob-Wan Kenobi are all Jedi Knights.

Jedi Master
The most experienced Jedi of all.

Jedi order
The name of a group that defends peace and justice in the galaxy.

Jedi Temple
The Jedi headquarters where the Jedi Council meets and Jedi live, train, and work.

Lightsaber
A Jedi's or Sith's weapon, made of glowing energy.

Light side
The part of the Force associated with goodness, compassion, and healing

Rebel
Someone who opposes whoever is in power.

Republic
A nation or group of nations in which the people vote for their leaders.

Senate
The governing body of the Republic.

Senator
A member of the Senate. He or she will have been chosen (elected) by the people of his or her country.

Sith
Enemies of the Jedi who use the dark side of the Force.

Stormtroopers
Soldiers, many of them clones, who are loyal to Emperor Palpatine. They wear white armor.

Index